CW00749871

I Am Always I

SAHAJA

First published in 2023 by Sahaja Publications

PO Box 887, Oxford OX1 9PR

www.sahajapublications.com

Text copyright © Rupert Spira 2023

Illustrations copyright © Zuzanna Celej 2023

The moral right of Rupert Spira to be identified as the author of this work has
been asserted in accordance with the Copyright, Designs and Patents Act 1988.

All rights reserved. No part of this publication may be reproduced or
transmitted in any form or by any means, electronic or mechanical,
including photocopying, recording or any information storage or retrieval
system, without prior permission in writing from the publisher.

ISBN 978–1–915635–13–6

Book design by Rob Bowden

Production, print, distribution and sales managed by Whitefox

Printed and bound by AllNote

*With gratitude to Zuzanna Celej, Ruth Middleton, Jacqueline Boyle,
Lynne Saner, Rob Bowden, Chris Wold, Amelia Collins and Julia Koppitz.*

I Am Always I

Rupert Spira

Illustrated by Zuzanna Celej

To the child in us all

I am not always happy

I don't always feel free

I am not always lonely

But I am always me.

I am not always naughty

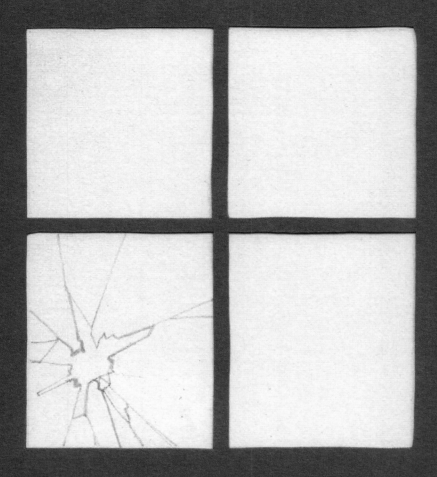

I don't often feel shy

I am not always hungry

But I am always I.

I am not always sleepy

I don't often cry

I am not always messy

But I am always I.

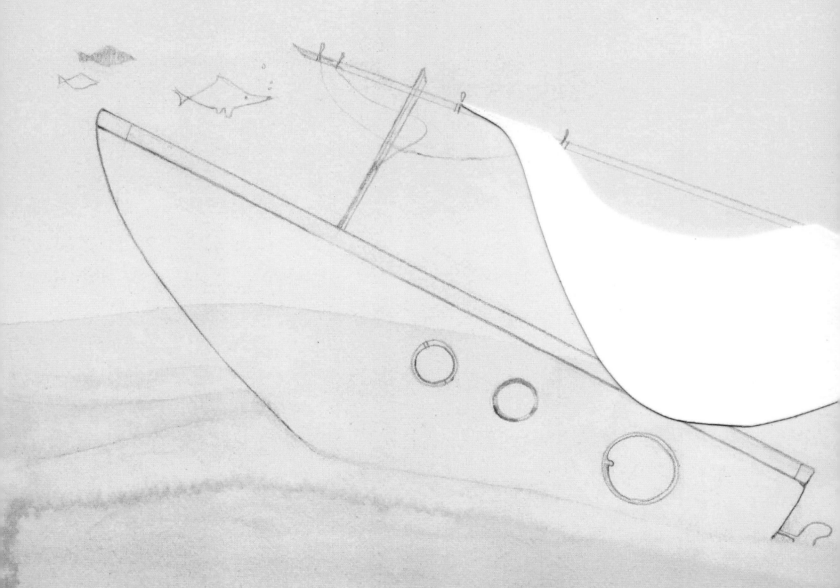

I am not always nice

I don't always try

I am sometimes forgetful

But I am always I.

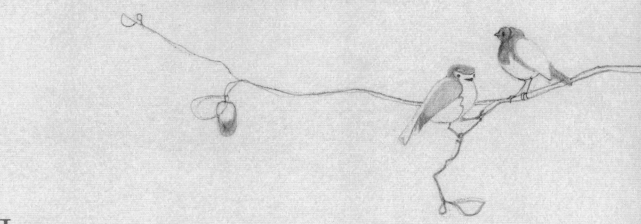

Once I was two

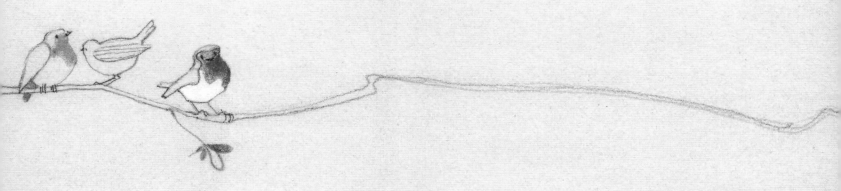

For a while I was three

I am not always four

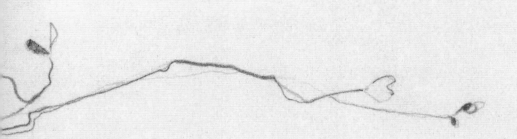

But I am always me.

Sometimes I'm lazy

But I don't ever lie

I am not always cheerful

But I am always I.

I am not always right

But I do what I can

I may not be perfect

But I am what I am.

Everything changes

So what can I be?

I cannot be anything

But I am always me.